·A·
NEW DAY

Grateful acknowledgment is made to the following publishers, authors, and agents for their permission to reprint copyrighted material. Any adaptations are noted in the individual acknowledgments and are made with the full knowledge and approval of the authors or their representatives. Every effort has been made to locate all copyright proprietors; any errors or omissions in copyright notice are inadvertent and will be corrected in future printings as they are discovered.

"Alanike and the Storyteller" by Donita Creola, © 1989 by Silver, Burdett & Ginn Inc.

"All of Our Noses Are Here" adapted from *All of Our Noses Are Here and Other Noodle Tales*. Retold by Alvin Schwartz. Pictures by Karen Ann Weinhaus. Text copyright © 1985 by Alvin Schwartz. Illustrations copyright © 1985 by Karen Ann Weinhaus. Reprinted by permission of Harper & Row, Publishers, Inc., and of the author's agents, Curtis Brown Ltd.

"Alone" excerpt adapted from *Days with Frog and Toad* by Arnold Lobel. Text and art copyright © 1979 by Arnold Lobel. Reprinted with permission of the American publishers, Harper and Row, Publishers, Inc., and of the British publishers, William Heinemann Ltd.

The Bear's Toothache written and illustrated by David McPhail. Copyright © 1972 by David McPhail. By permission of Little, Brown and Company.

"City" from *The Langston Hughes Reader* by Langston Hughes. Reprinted by permission of Harold Ober Associates Incorporated. Copyright © 1958 by Langston Hughes. Copyright renewed 1986 by George Houston Bass.

Dreams written and illustrated by Ezra Jack Keats, reprinted by permission of Macmillan Publishing Company. Copyright © 1974 Ezra Jack Keats.

"Goldfish and Lee" by Mitchell Sharmat, © 1989 by Silver, Burdett & Ginn Inc.

"Lee Bennett Hopkins Interviews Jerry Pinkney," © 1989 by Silver, Burdett & Ginn Inc.

"The Man, the Cat, and the Sky" by Barbara Juster Esbensen, © 1989 by Silver, Burdett & Ginn Inc.

"A New Day in the City" by Alice Benjamin Boynton, © 1989 by Silver, Burdett & Ginn Inc.

"Since Hanna Moved Away" from *If I Were in Charge of the World and Other Worries* by Judith Viorst. Copyright © 1981 Judith Viorst. Reprinted with the permission of the American publisher, Atheneum Publishers, an imprint of Macmillan Publishing Company, the author's American agents, Lescher & Lescher, Ltd., and of the author's British agents A. M. Heath & Company Ltd.

"Some Fun" written and illustrated by James Marshall, © 1989 by Silver, Burdett & Ginn Inc.

"Stone Soup" adapted by Marjorie and Mitchell Sharmat, © 1989 by Silver, Burdett & Ginn Inc.

Acknowledgments continue on page 256, which constitutes an extension of this copyright page.

WORLD OF READING

·A· NEW DAY

P. David Pearson   Dale D. Johnson

Theodore Clymer   Roselmina Indrisano   Richard L. Venezky

James F. Baumann   Elfrieda Hiebert   Marian Toth

Consulting Authors

Carl Grant   Jeanne Paratore

SILVER BURDETT & GINN

NEEDHAM, MA • MORRISTOWN, NJ
ATLANTA, GA • CINCINNATI, OH • DALLAS, TX
MENLO PARK, CA • DEERFIELD, IL

UNIT
ONE

STORYTELLERS

DIGGING ON THE SANDS.

UNIT ONE

FRIENDS FOREVER

We meet friends in school. We meet friends in books.

What makes a friend a friend?

DIGGING ON THE SANDS,
ceramic tiles c. 1900

YOUR FRIEND, LITTLE BEAR

from *Little Bear's Friend*

written by Else Holmelund Minarik
illustrated by Maurice Sendak

Summer is over, and Little Bear's friend must go back to school. Little Bear finds a way to stay friends.

Summer was over,
and Emily was saying good-by.
It was time to go
back to school.
Mother Bear baked a cake.
Little Bear made lemonade.

Mother Bear said,
"Let us eat up all the cake.
If we do, then it will not
rain tomorrow."

"Let it rain," said Little Bear.
"Emily will not be here tomorrow
to play with me."

So they ate the cake,
and drank the lemonade,
and talked and talked.

They talked until it was time
for Emily to go home.

Emily opened her pocketbook.
She took out a fine new pen.
"This is for you," she said.
"I want you to have it."

Little Bear took the pen.
"Thank you, Emily," he said.

He ran into his room,
and came back with a pretty
toy boat.

"This is for you," he said.
"For keeps.
You can sail it in your bathtub."

"Thank you," said Emily. "I will.
Good-by, Little Bear.
See you next summer."

Little Bear stood at the door
till Emily was out of sight.
Two big tears ran down his face.

Mother Bear saw them,
and took him on her lap.

"My goodness, Little Bear," she said.
"You will be going to school, too,
and you will learn to write.
Then you can write to Emily."

And soon he did write to Emily,
like this:

Dear Emily,

It is snowing.
I love the snow.
I wish I could send you some.
Owl, Duck, Hen, and Cat
send their love.
So do the ducklings.
I cannot wait for summer.

Your friend,
Little Bear

Reader's Response

Do you think that Emily's gift was
a good gift for Little Bear? Tell why
or why not.

YOUR FRIEND, LITTLE BEAR

Thinking It Over

1. Why was Emily going away?
2. Why did Little Bear give Emily a boat?
3. Was Little Bear sad to see Emily go? How do you know?
4. Tell what happened first, next, and last in the story.

Writing to Learn

THINK AND PRETEND You are Emily. You write a letter back to Little Bear. What would you say?

> Dear little Bear,
>   I liked your letter. I miss you and Owl, Duck, Cat, and Hen. I miss the ducklings, too.
>   Your friend,
>   Emily

WRITE On a piece of paper, write what you think Emily would say to Little Bear.

two friends

lydia and shirley have
two pierced ears and
two bare ones
five pigtails
two pairs of sneakers
two berets
two smiles
one necklace
one bracelet
lots of stripes and
one good friendship

Nikki Giovanni

Drawing Story Pictures

You can draw a picture about a story. Here is a picture someone drew about "Your Friend, Little Bear."

What is happening in the picture?

Read the poem "Our Mr. Toad" by David McCord. Draw a picture about the poem.

> Our Mr. Toad
> Has a nice abode
> Under the first front step.
> When it rains he's cool
> In a secret pool
> Where the water goes
>   drip
>   drop
>   drep.

What did you put in your picture?

Read the next story. Some questions will ask you to draw a picture. Try to answer the questions.

◆◆◆ The writing connection can be found on page 59.

Frog and Toad learn something new about being close friends.

Alone

from *Days with Frog and Toad*

written and illustrated
by Arnold Lobel

Toad went to Frog's house.

He found a note on the door.

The note said,

"Dear Toad, I am not at home.

I went out.

I want to be alone."

"Alone?" said Toad.

"Frog has me for a friend.

Why does he want to be alone?"

Toad went to the woods.

Frog was not there.

He went to the meadow.

Frog was not there.

Toad went down to the river.

There was Frog.

He was sitting on an island

by himself.

"Poor Frog," said Toad.

"He must be very sad.

I will cheer him up."

Toad ran home.

He made sandwiches.

He made a pitcher

of iced tea.

He put everything

in a basket. ◄►►

◄►►
**What picture
would you
draw about
Toad?**

Then Toad ran back to the river.

"Frog," he called, "it's me.

It's your best friend, Toad!"

Frog was too far away to hear.

A turtle swam by.

Toad got on the turtle's back.

"Turtle," said Toad,

"take me to the island.

Frog is there.

He wants to be alone."

What picture
would you
draw about
Toad?

29

"If Frog wants to be alone,"
said the turtle,
"why don't you leave him alone?"
"Maybe you are right," said Toad.
"Maybe Frog does not
want to see me.
Maybe he does not want me
to be his friend anymore."
"Yes, maybe," said the turtle
as he swam to the island.

"Frog!" called Toad.

"I am sorry for all

the silly things I do.

I am sorry for all

the silly things I say.

Please be my friend again!"

Toad slipped off the turtle.

With a splash, he fell

in the river. ❖

What picture would you draw about Toad?

Frog pulled Toad

up onto the island.

Toad looked in the basket.

The sandwiches were wet.

The pitcher of iced tea was empty.

"Our lunch is wet," said Toad.

"I made it for you, Frog,

so that you would be happy."

"But Toad," said Frog.

"I AM happy. I am very happy.

This morning

when I woke up

I felt good because

the sun was out.

I felt good because

I was a frog.

And I felt good because

I have you for a friend." ◆◆◆

◆◆◆
What picture would you draw about Frog and Toad?

Frog and Toad

stayed on the island all day.

They ate wet sandwiches

without iced tea.

They were two close friends

sitting alone together. ◆◆◆

Draw a picture about this story. Write or tell about your picture.

◆LIBRARY LINK◆

"Alone" came from a book called Days with Frog and Toad. *Look for it and other Frog and Toad books in your library.*

Reader's Response

What do good friends do together? What did Frog and Toad do together?

34

Alone

Thinking It Over

1. Why did Toad think that Frog was sad?
2. What is one thing Toad did to try to cheer up Frog?
3. Frog wanted to be alone. How do you know this?

Writing to Learn

THINK AND PRETEND   Frog left a note on his door for Toad. It said that Frog wanted to be alone. If you left a note for Toad, what would you write?

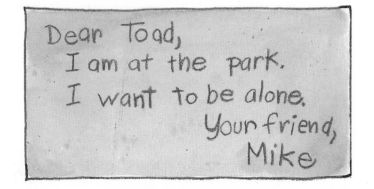

> Dear Toad,
>   I am at the park.
>   I want to be alone.
>   Your friend,
>   Mike

WRITE   On your paper write a note to Toad.

Magazine

News About Reading

Frogs in Stories

You have just read a story about a frog. Here are some famous frogs from other stories. Each artist draws frogs differently. Look at the pictures. Can you tell something different about each frog?

What things can you tell about this frog?

Or this frog?

Or this frog?

Which frog would you have
the most fun with?

You will meet another frog in this unit.
Here is what he looks like.

☛ **The frogs on this page are make-believe. If
you want to read about real frogs, find a magazine
in the library called "Your Big Backyard." It often
has pictures and articles about real frogs.**

A New Day in the City

by Alice Benjamin Boynton

*In this story, Benita finds a way
to cheer up a sick friend.*

It was a new day in the city.
The sun came up and woke Benita.

After breakfast, Mother said,
"It's a good day for a walk in the
park. Why not call Lisa? Maybe
she'd like to go for a walk with us."

"Lisa can't take a walk with us
because she is sick today. She has a
cold," said Benita. "We can still go."

So Mother and Benita walked
to the park. On the way, they saw
Mr. Green's dog, Missy. Missy sat
in a box by Mr. Green's chair.
She licked Benita's hand.

"She must want to tell us
something," Benita said to Mother.
"I wish she could talk."

When they came to the duck pond
in the park, the big white duck
quacked and quacked.

"What is it, duck?" Benita asked.
"I wish you could talk."

41

Then Mother said, "Benita,
look up!"

In the big tree sat the mother bird
and her three little birds. The mother
bird sang to Benita.

"She'd like to tell me something,
too," said Benita. "What could it be?
I wish she could talk."

The next day, Lisa was still sick.
After breakfast, Benita and Mother went
for a walk in the park.

Mr. Green called to Benita.
"Benita," he said. "Come and see
what Missy has to show you."

Missy was still in the box.
But now there were three little
tan puppies in the box, too.

"That's what she wanted to tell
you," said Mother.

When they got to the park,
Mother and Benita looked for the big
white duck. There she was with three
little ducks.

"Quack, quack, quack!" said
the mother duck.

"Oh," Benita laughed. "That's
what you wanted to tell me. I'm
sorry Lisa isn't here to meet your
ducklings."

44

Next, Benita looked for the little birds in the nest. Benita saw them flying away from the tree.

"Look, Mother," cried Benita. "The little birds can fly!"

"That must be what the mother bird wanted to tell us," said Mother.

45

"There are lots of surprises
in the city," said Benita. "I'll be
glad when Lisa is well again. I know
she'd like to see them, too. Wait!
I know a way to show her everything
I saw."

When Benita got home, she ran
to get some paints and paper. She
painted a picture of Missy and her
puppies. She painted the duck
family on the pond. She painted
the little birds flying from
the nest.

46

After Benita had painted the pictures,
she called Lisa.

Benita said, "I'm sorry you weren't
with us today. I miss you. You can't
go for a walk with me today. But I can
show you all the surprises Mother and
I saw. Just wait and see!"

The next afternoon Benita
and her mother took the pictures
to Lisa's house. Together they
put up the pictures in her room.
The room looked just like the park.
Lisa was so happy.

"I'm glad you're my friend,
Benita," she said. "I can't wait
to go for a walk with you. Then
we can look for all the new
things in the park."

 Reader's Response

Benita drew pictures of what she
saw in the park to cheer up Lisa. If
you were Benita, how would you have
cheered up Lisa?

48

A New Day in the City

Thinking It Over

1. What surprise did Missy have for Benita?
2. Name two ways in which Benita was a good friend to Lisa.
3. Where does Benita live? How do you know?

Writing to Learn

THINK AND DECIDE   If you were Mr. Green, what would you name Missy's puppies? Draw a picture of Missy and her puppies.

WRITE   Label Missy. Write the name you chose for each puppy on your picture.

CITY

by Langston Hughes

In the morning the city
Spreads its wings
Making a song
In stone that sings.

In the evening the city
Goes to bed
Hanging lights
About its head.

Together

by Anne Rockwell

Sometimes friends share what each can do well.

Carol is my best friend. We always work and play together. Carol is blind. She cannot see, but Carol can do other things. She is a good storyteller. When she tells stories, I write the words for her. Then I draw pictures to go with her words. I tell Carol what the pictures look like.

Carol can play the guitar.
I love to hear her play. Sometimes
I try to play the guitar, too.
Carol helps me. First she shows me
how to hold the guitar. Then she tells
me to feel the strings as I play.
We play and sing together.

Carol and I love to read together.
I read with my eyes. Carol reads with
her fingers. Her books are special.
The words are made with dots.
People who are blind feel the dots
to read the words.

Carol shows me how she reads.
I can feel the dots with my fingers.
I try to read the dots, but I can't.
Carol reads them for me.

Carol and I have our own garden.
It is work to plant a garden.
My dad helps. He finds seeds
for us to plant.

First, we plant the seeds
in the ground. Then we water them.
My dad helps us put water in the
watering can. Sometimes I can't hold
the watering can. Carol and I
do it together.

Then we wait for the first
plants to come up. At last a little
green plant pops up out of the ground.
Carol and I run to tell my dad.
I tell Carol about the plant
and she feels it with her fingers.
It is a special day for us.

Carol and I love to work
and play together. We always have
a lot of fun. We are glad that
we can share so many special things.

 Reader's Response

What did you learn from reading
this story? Tell what you know now
that you did not know before.

Together

◆ Thinking It Over

1. How did Carol help her friend?
2. Why did Carol read with her fingers?
3. Carol liked her friend. What tells you this?
4. Tell the order in which Carol and her friend planted their garden.

◆ Writing to Learn

THINK AND DRAW   Friends share. What would you like to share with Carol if she were your friend? Draw a picture of you and Carol.

WRITE   Write some words about Carol. Tell what you and Carol are doing.

Reading Social Studies

Words and pictures in your social studies book tell you about people and places. Pictures show you what people look like and where they live. They show you things people do. Sometimes they can show you how people feel.

What are the people doing in this picture?

Did you answer that people are feeding hay to the horse? Can you tell the time of year?

What is happening in the picture below?

Here are some clues. The door looks big, like a school door. The boy has a lunch box in his hand. Did you say that the boy is going to school?

As You Read   Read the following pages from a social studies book. Answer the questions on page 65.

How do family members help one another?

Family members help each other.

They help each other work.
They help each other learn.

What are some days families celebrate?

Families **celebrate** special days.
Birthdays are special days.

Holidays are special days.

Using What You Have Learned

1. You learn on page 62 that family members help one another. What are the family members doing to help one another?

2. Look at the picture of the father and the boy on page 63. What are the father and boy doing?

3. Look at the picture at the top of page 64. How do you think the grandfather feels?

4. What is happening in the picture at the bottom of page 64?

Examples and excerpts are from *Families and Their Needs, Silver Burdett & Ginn Social Studies,* © 1988.

Goldfish
and Lee

by Mitchell Sharmat

*When Lee visits Terry, he meets
an unexpected friend.*

This is a big day. Mom and I are going to visit my cousin, Terry. Terry lives on a farm. I live in the city with my mom. Sometimes Terry visits me in the city. Then I have to teach him how to do a lot of things. And Terry always has something new to teach me about the farm. Today he's going to show me how to ride his new horse!

Soon Mom and I are at Terry's farm. We see lots of people working. We see sheep, hens, and cows. But where is Terry's horse? I have never been close to a horse before, and I can't wait to ride it.

"Look over there, Lee," says Mom. "There's a horse near the barn. It looks golden in the sun. Terry's near the barn, too."

I start to run to Terry and the
horse. But then I stop. The horse
looks so big! When I get close to it,
I feel as small as an ant.

Terry smiles when I tell him how
small I feel. So I say, "Don't you feel
small when you come to the city?"

"Well, yes," Terry says and smiles.
"Sometimes I do."

Terry tries to help me.

"Talk to Goldfish," he says.

So I say, "Hello, Goldfish.
My name is Lee. How are you?"

Goldfish shakes his head.

"That means hello," Terry says.
"Now rub his nose."

So I reach out and rub Goldfish's
nose. It feels as soft as fur.

By now I can tell that I'm going
to like this horse.

"Do you want to ride him?"
Terry asks.

"Sure," I say. Then I get on
Goldfish, the horse.

"Hold on," says Terry. "I'm going
to take you for a walk." He leads
Goldfish across the grass.

"This is fun," I tell Terry.

Terry smiles. "I thought you'd
like it," he says.

"Now watch this," Terry says.
"You'll see why his name is
Goldfish."

Terry leads Goldfish to the water.
What do you think Goldfish does?
He puts his nose under the water
and blows into it!

"You see?" Terry laughs.
"He thinks he's a fish!"

73

Too soon I have to say goodbye
to Goldfish and Terry.

"That Goldfish is a neat horse,"
I tell Terry. "You can be sure I'll
be back soon to ride him!"

 Reader's Response

Would you like to ride Goldfish?
Tell why or why not.

74

Goldfish and Lee

Thinking It Over

1. Where did Lee live? Where did Terry live?
2. Why did Lee stop running when he got close to Goldfish?
3. How did Terry help Lee learn to ride a horse?
4. When Terry visits the city, what do you think Lee will show him? Why do you think this?

Writing to Learn

THINK AND DISCOVER Would you like to visit the farm where Terry lives? Think about what you would see and do there.

WRITE Write what you would see and do.

75

Since Hanna Moved Away

The tires on my bike are flat.
The sky is grouchy gray.
At least it sure feels like that
Since Hanna moved away.

Chocolate ice cream tastes like prunes.
December's come to stay.
They've taken back the Mays and Junes
Since Hanna moved away.

Flowers smell like halibut.
Velvet feels like hay.
Every handsome dog's a mutt
Since Hanna moved away.

Nothing's fun to laugh about.
Nothing's fun to play.
They call me, but I won't come out
Since Hanna moved away.

Judith Viorst

We Are **BEST** Friends

written and illustrated by Aliki

Robert and Peter find a way to stay friends even though Peter must move far away.

Peter came to tell Robert the news.
"I am moving away," he said.

"You can't move away," said Robert.
"We are best friends."

"I am moving far away," said Peter.

"What will you do without me?"
asked Robert.
"Who will you play with?"

"We will live in a new house,"
said Peter.

"You will miss my birthday!"
said Robert.

"I will be going to a new school,"
said Peter.

"Who will you play with?"
asked Robert. "No one can play like
best friends."

"I will make new friends," said Peter.

"You can't move away," said Robert.
"You will miss me too much."

But Peter moved away.
There was nothing to do without Peter.
There was no one to play with.
There was no one to share with.
There was no fun anymore.

"Hello. My name is Will,"
said a new face.
"I used to go to another school.
My friends are there."

"I don't like the name Will,"
thought Robert.

"It was fun," said Will.
"Not like this place."

A letter came for Robert.
A letter from Peter.

Dear Robert,
   I like my new house now.
   I like my new school now.
   I didn't like anything when
                          I got here.

But now I have a friend, Alex.
You are my best friend,
but Alex is nice.
It is fun to have someone to play
with again.
It's not so lonely.
                Your best friend,
                   Peter

Robert drew Peter a letter.
He drew two friends on their bikes.
He wrote:

If you were here,
this is what we'd be doing.
But you're not.

Then he wrote:

There is a new boy in school.

Robert saw Will.

"Did you lose something?" he asked.

"I thought I saw a frog," said Will.

"That's funny, looking for a frog,"
said Robert.

"What's funny about it?
I like frogs," said Will.

"I know where there are frogs,"
said Robert.
"Right in my garden."

"You're just saying that," said Will.

"I mean it," said Robert.
"You can see for yourself."

"If I had a frog in my garden,
I'd share it," said Will.

"That's what I'm doing," said Robert.

Robert and Will rode home together.
They went into the garden.
The frogs were there.
One jumped under a bush, and Will got it.
"You like me, don't you?"

"The frogs lay their eggs here each year," said Robert.
"My friend Peter used to come watch the tadpoles.
He'll miss them."

"Why?" asked Will.

"He moved away," said Robert.
"Just about the time you came.
I write him letters."

"Then you can write about the tadpoles," said Will.

Robert wrote to Peter.

Dear Peter,
I can't wait until summer
when you come to visit.
The new boy is called Will.
I showed him the frogs.
He had a pet one near his home,
but he had to move away, like you.

Love,
Robert

P.S. How is Alex?
P.P.S. See you soon.

Robert mailed the letter,
then rode over to Will's house to play.

♦ LIBRARY LINK ♦

*Look in the library for these
books written and illustrated by Aliki:*
Digging Up Dinosaurs *and* Feelings.

Reader's **Response**

What part of this story would
you like to read to a good friend?

We Are **BEST** Friends

Thinking It Over

1. What news did Peter tell Robert in the beginning of the story?
2. When was Robert sad? What makes you think so?
3. What happened first in the story? What happened last?

Writing to Learn

THINK AND MAKE BELIEVE   Make believe Peter is your friend. What would you say if you were writing to him?

Dear Peter,
I made a snowman today. I put a hat on his head. He is holding a broom. I wish you could see him.
Your friend,
Mary

WRITE   Write a letter to Peter on your paper.

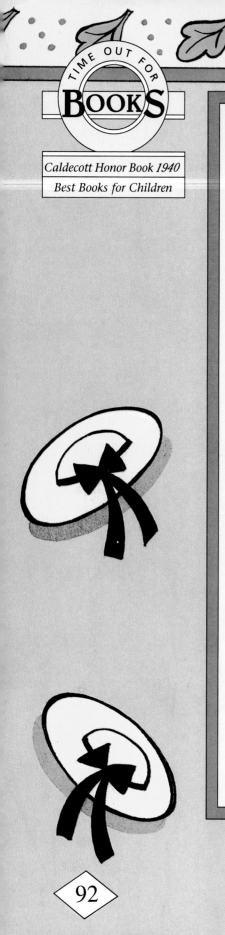

MADELINE

LUDWIG BEMELMANS

In an old house in Paris that was covered with vines lived twelve little girls in two straight lines. from *Madeline* by Ludwig Bemelmans

Madeline is a special book about a very special French girl. Millions of children around the world love *Madeline*. Some children read it in English. Other children read it in French or Japanese.

Ludwig Bemelmans made up the story of *Madeline* when he was sick in the hospital. He got the idea when he met a girl who was also sick, but she wasn't afraid.

What makes Madeline such a popular girl? For one thing, she is very brave. For another, she likes adventure.

You may want to read *Madeline* to find out about her adventure in the middle of the night.

Some Fun

written and illustrated
by James Marshall

Do friends have to like the same things? A dog and a goldfish like different things.

A dog and her goldfish were
sitting by the fire.

"I want to have some fun," said
the goldfish.

"But this is fun," said the dog.

"Not really," said the goldfish.
"I want to go places and see things.
I want to see the woods, the sky, and
the sea. I want to see some sharks!"

"Oh, very well," said the dog.

"This is very kind of you," said the goldfish.

"Anything to keep you happy," said the dog. "But we can't go too far from home. We don't want to get lost."

"Where will we go first?" asked the goldfish.

"I know a place to see some sharks," said the dog. "It's not far."

"Oh, my!" cried the goldfish.
"Sharks! Look at their teeth!
This is really fun!"

"I'm glad you think so," said
the dog. "Now can we go home?"

"Oh, no!" cried the goldfish.
"I want to do more! Now I want
to see the sea."

"Anything to keep you happy,"
said the dog.

"Look at the waves!" cried
the goldfish. "This is really fun!"

But the dog did not like the sea.
"The waves make me feel sick,"
she said. "Now can we go home?"

"Oh, no!" said the goldfish.
"Now I want to see the sky. I want
to fly."

"Anything to keep you happy," said the dog.

"This is really fun!" cried the goldfish. "Look at all the hills!"

But the dog did not like to fly. "I can't look down," she said. "I can't. Now can we go home?"

"Oh, no!" said the goldfish.
"Before we go home, we must see
the woods."

"Anything to keep you happy,"
said the dog.

"Oh, my!" cried the goldfish.
"Look at all the trees."

The two friends looked all around
the woods. Before long they were lost.

"I'm sorry," said the dog.
"I don't know how to get home."

"Are you lost?" asked a
kind elephant.

"Yes, we are," said the goldfish.

"Then I will take you home,"
said the elephant.

"This is very kind of you,"
said the dog.

"It is fun to go places and
see things," said the elephant.
"But it is good to go home, too."

"Yes, it is," said the dog.

Before long the dog and her
goldfish were home.

"That was so much fun," said
the goldfish. "Where will we go now?"

"Now we will sit at home by
the fire," said the dog. "That is what
I want to do."

"Anything to keep you happy,"
said the goldfish.

"You are very kind," said the dog.

Reader's Response

Did you smile when you read this story? What part made you smile the most?

Writing a Letter

You have read about friends. Friends like to get letters. You can write a letter to one of your friends.

Getting Ready

All letters have a beginning, a middle, and an end. Look at the letter below. Use it to help you plan your letter.

Dear _____(beginning)_____,

_____

(middle)

_____

_____

Your friend,

(end) _____

Writing

Look at how this letter begins and ends. Begin your letter the same way. In the middle, write what you want to say to your friend. End your letter by writing your name.

Listening to My Writing

Read your letter aloud. Do you have any other news you want to tell your friend?

Sharing

Ask someone at home to help you write the envelope. Then put a stamp on it and mail it.

Making a Greeting Card

Terry lived far away from Lee. If Lee wanted to tell Terry something, he could send a greeting card.

Now you and a friend will work together to make a card. As you work, make sure you:

♦ Help each other think of ideas.

♦ Listen when the other person talks.

Dear Terry,
k you for
ride
goldfish
r horse.
as fun!
i Lee

First gather the things you need to make a card. Then think of some classmates who would like to receive a card. Choose one person.

Think of some ideas for pictures to put on the card. You can each draw one picture on the card.

Will your card be a surprise?

May I Bring a Friend? by Beatrice Schenk de Regniers *(Atheneum, 1964).* Each time a boy has tea with the King and Queen, he brings along a friend—an animal that causes many problems.

Friends by Helme Heine *(Atheneum, 1982).* A pig, a rooster, and a mouse cannot fit into each other's houses. They agree that friends do not have to spend *every* moment together.

My Friend John by Charlotte Zolotow *(Harper & Row, 1968).* Two young boys do things differently, but they are still best friends!

UNIT TWO

STORYTELLERS

*W*hat makes a
story so special
that you want
to hear it over
and over again?

PAINTED BOX,
Russian, contemporary

109

Worlds I Know

by Myra Cohn Livingston

Some stories take you to places
you have never gone before.

Once upon a time

I can read the pictures
by myself
in the books that lie
on the lowest shelf.
I know the place
where the stories start
and some I can even say
by heart,
and I make up adventures
and dreams and words
for some of the pages
I've never heard.

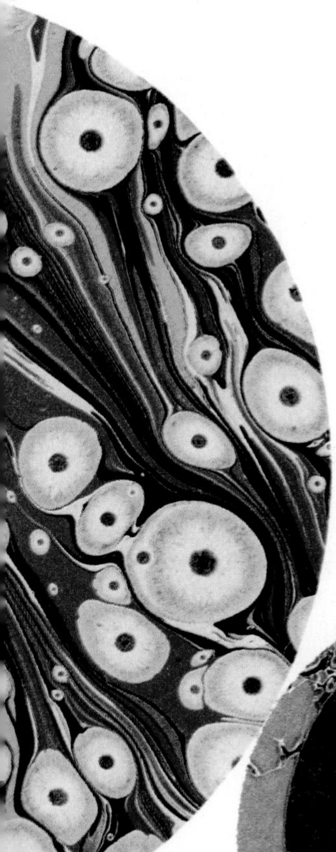

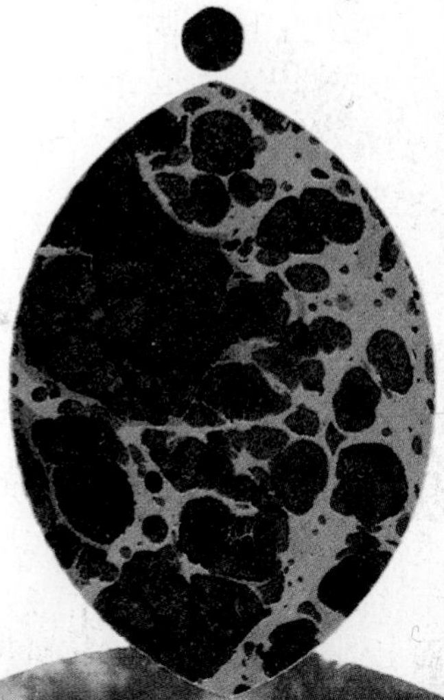

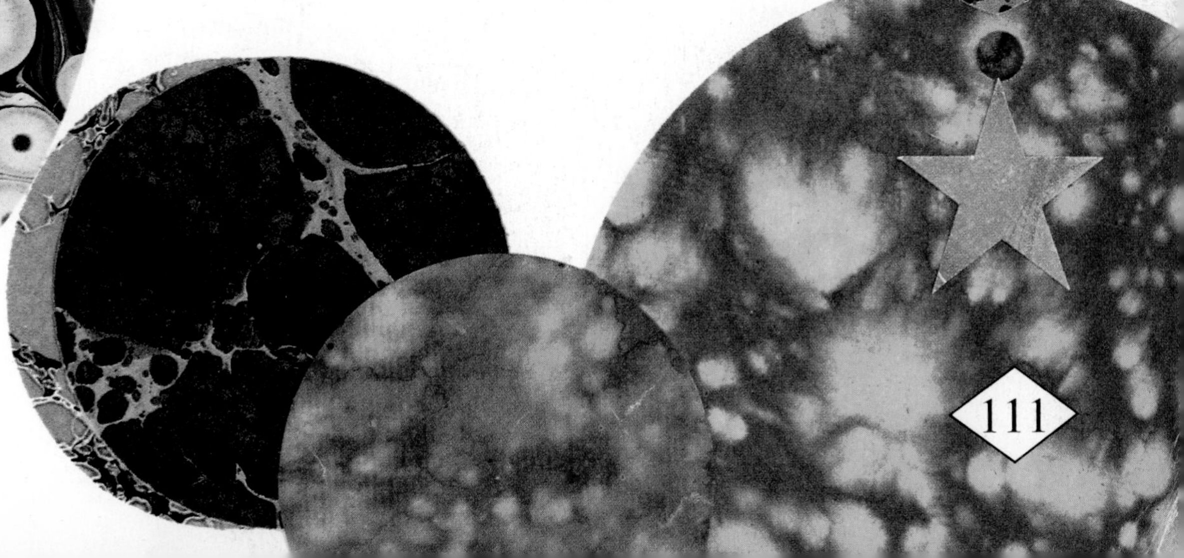

But I like it best
when Mother sits
and reads to me
my favorites;
when Rapunzel pines
and the prince comes forth,
or the Snow Queen sighs
in the bitter north;
when Rose Red snuggles
against the bear,
and I lean against Mother
and feel her hair.

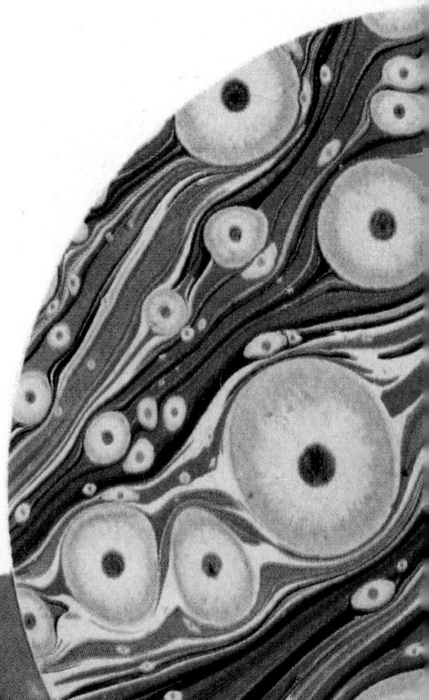

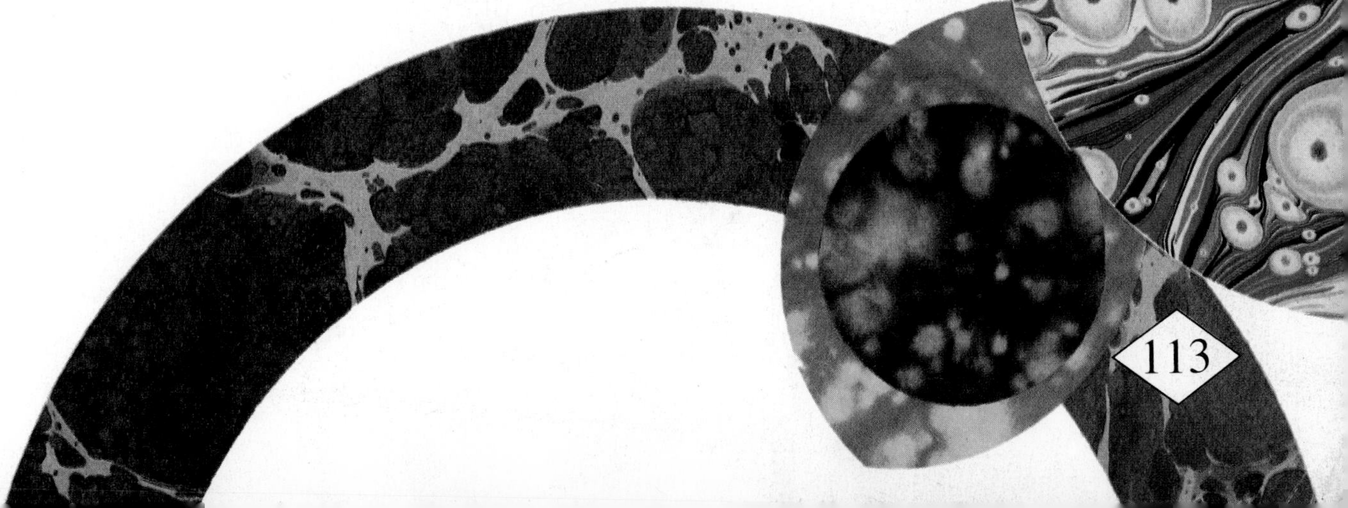

We look at stars
in Hungary—
back of the North Wind—
over the sea—
the Nutcracker laughs;
the Erl King calls;
a wish comes true;
the beanstalk falls;
the Western wind
blows sweet and low,
and Mother gives words
to worlds I know.

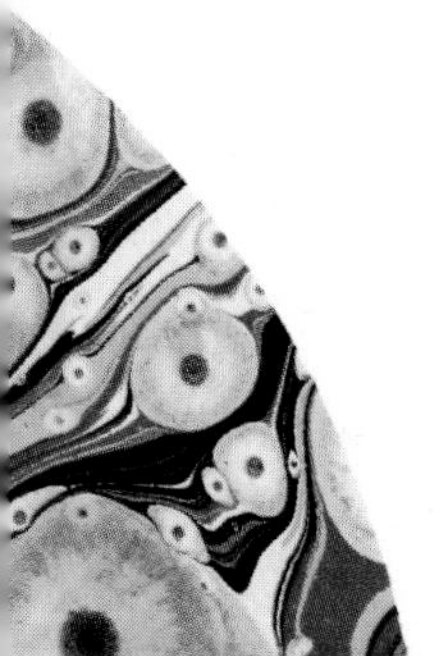

Reader's Response

What worlds do you know about from your favorite stories?

Worlds I Know

Thinking It Over

1. What kind of stories was this poem about? How do you know?
2. Is it fun to have a grown-up read stories aloud? Why or why not?
3. What are some favorite stories that you like to have read to you?

Writing to Learn

THINK AND IMAGINE   Draw a person or animal from your favorite story.

WRITE   On your paper, write "Once upon a time..." Then tell one thing that happened in your picture.

117

LITERATURE LINK

What can you do when stories don't make sense?

Once upon a time

"**W**orlds I Know" is all about stories that take readers to make-believe places.

But sometimes, stories with make-believe things don't seem to make sense. You can get mixed up. Try these tips if that happens.

Is It Make-Believe?

If something doesn't make sense, stop reading and think for a minute. Think about the story. Go back to the part where you got mixed up. Ask yourself, "Could this be something make-believe?"

Sometimes the pictures can help you, too. They might show you what is happening in the story.

The next story, "The Man, the Cat, and the Sky," is about make-believe things. When you read it, remember these tips.

The Man, the Cat, and the Sky

by Barbara Juster Esbensen

See how clouds help the man in this story.

Once upon a time there was a man. He had a big white cat called Cream. Their house and garden were by a river in the country. In the morning they would look at the green water. They would listen to the blue wind blow over the grass. The man would work in his garden. Cream would watch the colored fish swim by in the water.

One morning, the man was sad.
Today the king and his friends would
be playing games. The man wanted to
go over the far hills to watch.

"I have never watched a king play
games," he told Cream. "I would like
to go, but I don't have a horse or
even a tiny cart. How could we get
there? It is too far for us to walk."

121

Cream looked sad. He wanted to see a king's cat. Maybe the king's cat played games, too.

The man stopped and looked up at the sky. It was as blue as could be. Then the man saw a big puff of white.

"I see a big ship up there, Cream!" he said. "Maybe that ship can take us to see the king. What do you think?"

Cream looked up. The ship was
blowing away.

"Oh, no!" said the man. "We'll
never get there! That ship can't
take us to see the king's games."

The man turned to look at the sky
again. "Now there are three white
horses in the sky," he said. "Would
you like to go with me to the king's
town, Cream? We could race like the
wind on the backs of these white horses.
One horse is for you, one horse is for
me. One horse will show us the way to
go. What do you think, Cream?"

Cream looked up. The horses
were blowing away.

"Oh, no!" said the man. "Now
we can't go to see the king on the
white horses!"

The man turned and looked up again.
There was nothing to see this time.
There was just the blue sky everywhere.
"Now we will never see the king,"
he told Cream.

Cream did not hear the man's
sad words. He was listening to
something else. Cream could hear
singing far up the river. Now the
man listened, too.

It was the king! The king and
his friends were singing and blowing
their whistles. They came sailing
down the river. Their little ship
was filled with bright red tents.

The man said, "It is the king!
Can this be true, Cream?"

Cream looked at the king and his black cat and the red tents. The wind did not blow them away.

The man sat down and took Cream on his lap. They watched the king and his friends play their games.

◆ Reader's Response

Do you think what the man saw in the clouds was real? Tell why or why not.

The Man, the Cat, and the Sky

Thinking It Over

1. Why was the man sad at the beginning of the story? How do you know this?
2. What did the man see in the sky?
3. Why did the things the man saw blow away?
4. Which of these story words would come first in the dictionary: *man, cat, sky, king, wind?* Why?

Writing to Learn

THINK AND LOOK When you look into the sky, what do you see? Look at this picture of the sky. What animals do you see?

WRITE Make a list of what you see in the picture.

129

In this story, three hungry people play a trick to get something to eat.

Stone Soup

adapted by Marjorie and Mitchell Sharmat

Three travelers were on their way home. They walked through woods. They walked through meadows.

"I need to eat," said the first traveler.

"I need to sleep," said the second traveler.

"I need to eat and sleep," said the third traveler.

They kept walking down the road until they came to a little town.

The people in the town saw the three travelers coming down the road.

"They will want a place to eat and sleep," said one man. "What can we do?"

"Tell them the wolf ate all our
food! Then we can hide it," said
a second man.

"We can hide it under our beds,"
said a third.

The people ran to hide their food.
Some people hid it under their beds.
Some people hid their food in other places.

The three travelers came to the town.

"We have walked and walked," they said to the people. "May we have some food and a place to sleep?"

"A wolf ate all our food," said the people in the town.

"All we have is water," they said.

"Water!" the three travelers said. "Good! We can make stone soup with that."

"What is stone soup?" asked
a woman.

"We'll show you," said the first
traveler. "Find us a big pot. Then
bring us some water and three, big
flat stones. Then get us some sticks
for a fire."

The people ran to get the pot, the water, and the sticks. Then they got the three, big, flat stones.

The travelers put the water and stones in the pot. Then they lit a fire under the pot. The fire cooked the stone soup.

The first traveler ate some soup. "M-m-m," he said. "The soup is good now. But green beans and a turnip would make it better."

"You're right! The wolf did not eat all my green beans," said one woman. She ran home and took the beans from under her bed.

"And I have a turnip," said another woman. She ran home and took the turnip from under a basket.

The travelers put the beans and the turnip into the pot.

"M-m-m. Smell the soup! It is better now," said the second traveler. "But peas and beets would make it even better. Can you find some?"

"You're right! It does smell good," said a woman.

"The wolf did not eat all my peas and beets," said one man. "I think I still have some at my house." And he ran to get them.

"Here," he said when he came back. He put the peas and beets into the pot.

"M-m-m. Smell the soup now. It is much better," said the third traveler. "But meat would make it much, much better. That is what the queen has in her soup."

"You ate with the queen?" the people asked in surprise.

Then they took all their food and put it into the pot.

"M-m-m!" said the people.

"M-m-m!" said the travelers. "This is soup fit for a queen!"

"You're wise men to make real soup from stones," said the people.

"Wise men need sleep," said the travelers.

"Take our beds!" said the people.

The three men went to sleep for the night. The next day they went off down the road to the next town.

 **R**eader's Response

If you were in the village, what questions would you ask the travelers?

STONE SOUP

Thinking It Over

1. What two things did the travelers need when they came to the town?
2. How did the travelers get food from the people to make stone soup?
3. How did the travelers make stone soup? Name the steps.
4. Do you think the travelers were wise men? Tell why you think so.

Writing to Learn

THINK AND DECIDE   Draw a soup pot.

WRITE   Draw what you would put in your pot. Write your own soup recipe.

Magazine

News About Reading

Story Songs

Sometimes stories are told through music. Raffi is a man who sings stories for children all over the world. He sometimes uses rhymes we all know, like "Baa Baa Black Sheep." Other times he makes up new songs to tell a story. He did this for "Baby Beluga."

☞ If you like story songs, look for song books in your library. Do you have a favorite story you would like to write a song for?

This is the beluga whale
in one of Raffi's songs.

Raffi is singing a story song.

Ella Jenkins sings stories, too. In some
of her songs, she sings a rhyme over and
over again. It's fun to clap along with her
story songs.

Singing a story helps you remember it
in a special way.

Ella Jenkins makes story songs fun.

Ella Jenkins Presents
My Street Begins
At My House
and other songs and rhythms
from "The Me Too Show"

Alanike
and the
Storyteller

written by Donita Creola
illustrated by Jerry Pinkney

Sometimes a boy or a girl in a story may be just like you.

Alanike was a little girl who lived in a small village in Africa. She went to the village school every day. She worked hard. She wanted to know everything about everything. Sometimes Alanike worked so hard there was no time to play with the other boys and girls.

Lee Bennett Hopkins
INTERVIEWS

Jerry Pinkney

This is Jerry Pinkney. He draws pictures of many things. He draws pictures for books. He draws pictures for stamps too.

These two stamps show pictures of famous Americans. One stamp shows Harriet Tubman. The other stamp shows Dr. Martin Luther King, Jr.

"My first love is drawing pictures for books," says Pinkney. "I hope that my pictures will help others want to read and look at books."

155

"As a child I drew everything," he said. "In school I drew and drew. My drawings made me feel special. I never thought I would grow up one day to be an artist. My mother always told me that I could be anything I wanted to be."

"I work with a pencil in one hand and an eraser in the other. I begin with a simple drawing," says Mr. Pinkney.

"If I don't like something that I draw, I erase it. Then I do it all over again. I work on it until I am happy with the drawing."

157

You saw some of Mr. Pinkney's drawings in "Alanike and the Storyteller." You can also look in the library for books with Mr. Pinkney's pictures:

The Patchwork Quilt
   by Valerie Flourney
Wild Wild Sunflower Child Anna
   by Nancy White Carlstrom

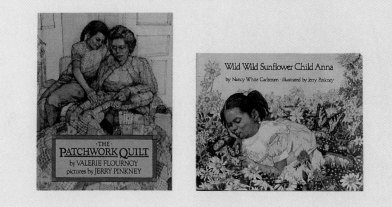

Reader's Response

Mr. Pinkney says, "If I don't like something that I draw, I erase it." What do you do if you don't like something that you draw?

LEE BENNETT HOPKINS INTERVIEWS

Jerry Pinkney

◆ Thinking It Over

1. Why does Mr. Pinkney enjoy drawing?
2. Mr. Pinkney wants his pictures to be just right. How do you know this?
3. Would you like to see some of Jerry Pinkney's books? Tell why or why not.

◆ Writing to Learn

THINK AND CHOOSE Jerry Pinkney draws pictures for stamps. Draw an outline of a stamp. Show your favorite person on your stamp.

WRITE Tell who is on your stamp. Write a sentence about your stamp.

Here is a story about two people who had three wishes!

The Three Wishes

by Verna Aardema

Fritz and Anna lived on a farm.
It was a small farm. It was also very
dry, and things did not grow well.
So Fritz and his wife, Anna, were poor.

One day there was a tap, tap, tap on
the door. A woman had come to the farm.
She had been walking most of the day,
and she was hungry. She asked Fritz
and Anna to give her something to eat.
Fritz and Anna had a pot of soup.
They let the woman come in to eat.

"Thank you," said the woman.
"You have been most kind. I will grant
you three wishes. Remember to use your
wishes wisely. Each wish you make will
come true."

"Thank you," said Fritz.

"Thank you very much," said Anna.

The woman left.

As soon as the woman was outside the door, Anna said, "Three wishes! Oh, Fritz, I've never been so happy! We can have anything we want!"

Fritz said, "Let's have one wish for you, and one wish for me. Then we will have one wish left for the two of us together."

"I like that," said Anna. "It will be fun to have one wish that is all mine."

For most of the day, Fritz and
Anna talked about the three wishes they
would make. They talked long after it was
time to eat again, and they forgot to
cook. They began to get hungry.

By the time Anna and Fritz made
soup, they were both very, very hungry.
As they sat down to eat, Fritz said, "I
wish we had a sausage to go with this
soup."

And there on the table was a
great big brown sausage!

"Oh, Fritz," said Anna, "there goes your wish! And we have only ONE sausage! I wish we had many, many sausages."

There was Anna's only wish!

PUM, PUM, PUM! Great big sausages rained down on them. They both ducked and tried to get the sausages off them.

"Enough! Enough!" cried Anna. "Get the sausages off me!"

"I can't help you," said Fritz. "I can't get the sausages off me!"

PUM, PUM, PUM, came the sausages. Soon the sausages were all around them.

"What can we do?" asked Anna, from under the sausages.

From under the sausages, Fritz said, "Let's eat them."

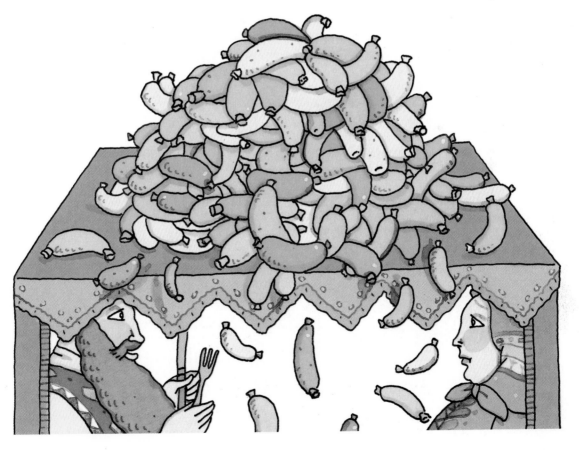

"Don't talk that way," said Anna.
"This is not funny! I've had enough
sausages. What can we do to get
out of this?"

"Well," said Fritz, "your wish
is gone, and mine is gone. But together
we have one wish left. Let's WISH to
get out from under the sausages."

Then they both said, "We wish
the sausages would go away."

Just as they had come, the
sausages went away. There were no
sausages anywhere! The big sausage
was also gone from the table.

Fritz and Anna were at the table,
with only the soup to eat.

"Oh, Fritz," said Anna, "I am so sad! Here we are without any more wishes."

"Anna," said Fritz, "we were happy before the woman came. We can be happy again. Most of all, I wish we had a sausage to eat with this soup."

"Oh, Fritz," said Anna, "I don't want to SEE a sausage for a long time!"

◆ LIBRARY LINK ◆

If you liked this story by Verna Aardema, look for her book Why Mosquitoes Buzz in People's Ears.

Reader's Response

How do you think Fritz and Anna felt when it began raining sausages? How do you think they felt when they used their last wish and the sausages disappeared?

The Three Wishes

◆ Thinking It Over

1. How did Fritz and Anna use up their three wishes?
2. If Fritz and Anna had three more wishes, what might they wish for? What makes you think this?
3. Why do you think the woman told them to use their wishes wisely?

◆ Writing to Learn

THINK AND PLAN   In this story, Fritz and Anna used up their wishes. Think about what could have happened.

1.	They could have wished for bread.
2.	They could have wished for more wishes.
3.	They could have not used the wishes.

WRITE   Use one of the ideas on this page or your own ideas to make up a new ending for the story.

169

All of Our Noses Are Here

retold by Alvin Schwartz
illustrated by Karen Ann Weinhaus

Mr. Brown has a problem.
Someone is missing.

The Browns went for a ride
in their rowboat. When the sun
began to go down, they rowed back
to shore.

"Everyone line up," said
Mr. Brown. "Let us see if anyone
fell out of the boat.

One is here.
Two are here.
Three are here.
And four are here."

171

"But we are five," said Mrs. Brown.

"I think I counted wrong," said
Mr. Brown. "I will count again.

One is here.
Two are here.
Three are here.
And four are here."

"Only four?" asked Mrs. Brown.

"Yes," said Mr. Brown. "One of
us is missing."

172

Mrs. Brown began to cry. So did the others.

"Why are all of you crying?" a fisherman asked.

"Five of us went rowing," said Mr. Brown. "But only four came back."

"Are you sure?" the fisherman asked.

Mr. Brown counted again.
Again he counted only four.

"I know what is wrong," said
the fisherman. "You forgot to count
yourself."

"I will try again," said
Mr. Brown.

"One is here.
Two are here.
Three are here.
And four are here.
And five are here.
And SIX are here!"

"But there should be five," said
Mrs. Brown.

"No," said Mr. Brown. "Now we are six."

"But I do not see anybody else," said Mrs. Brown.

They looked in the rowboat and
under the dock and up in the trees and
behind all the bushes, but they did not
find anyone.

"Come out! Come out! Whoever you
are!" Mr. Brown called.

The others called too, but nobody came out.

When the fisherman heard the calling, he went to see what was wrong.

"Now there are six of us, not five," said Mr. Brown. "But we cannot find this extra person."

"Are you sure there are six?" the
fisherman asked.

Mr. Brown counted again, and again
he counted six.

"You are doing it all wrong," said
the fisherman. "You counted yourself twice.
Let me show you the right way to count."

"Everybody, get down on your hands and knees. Now stick your noses into the mud and pull them out. Now count the holes your noses made."

Mr. Brown counted.

"One is here.
Two are here.
Three are here.
Four are here.
And FIVE are here."

181

"All of our noses are here!" he said. "Now we can go home."

♦LIBRARY LINK♦

"All of Our Noses Are Here" came from a book called All of Our Noses Are Here and Other Noodle Tales. *Look for it in your library.*

Reader's Response

Did you think this was a funny story? Tell why or why not.

All of Our Noses Are Here

Thinking It Over

1. Why did Mr. Brown count noses?
2. Mrs. Brown cried when Mr. Brown only counted *four* people. Why do you think she cried?
3. What happened when Mr. Brown counted noses?
4. Name one thing that tells you that this story is make-believe.

Writing to Learn

THINK AND INVENT   Mr. Brown needs to learn how to count. How would you teach him?

WRITE   One way to teach him is with a counting book. Make a counting book.

HARPER TROPHY

WHERE THE WILD THINGS ARE

STORY AND PICTURES BY MAURICE SENDAK

And when he came to the place where the wild things are they roared their terrible roars and gnashed their terrible teeth . . .

from *Where the Wild Things Are* by Maurice Sendak

Maurice Sendak has written many books. He wants them to be an adventure for children. He says that *Where the Wild Things Are* is one of his favorite books. Millions of children around the world think so, too. Sometimes children write letters to Maurice Sendak. They want to know how to get to where the wild things are.

If you read *Where the Wild Things Are*, you will sail to a faraway island and meet the wild things with a boy named Max. Will Max become king of the wild things?

*A boy solves a bear's
problem in a clever way.*

THE BEAR'S
TOOTHACHE

written and illustrated
by DAVID McPHAIL

One night I heard something
outside my window.

It was a bear
with a toothache.

I invited him in
and examined his teeth.

When I found the one that ached,
I tried to pull it out.
It wouldn't budge.

"Maybe some steak will loosen it
a little," said the bear.
So we went down to the kitchen,
where the bear chewed on some steak
and anything else he could find.
Pretty soon the food was all gone,
but the tooth was no looser
than before.

When we got back to my room,
I tried to hit the tooth with my pillow.
But the bear ducked,
and I hit the lamp instead
and knocked it to the floor.
Crash!

The noise woke my father,
who got up and came to my room.
"What happened to the lamp?"
he asked.
"It fell on the floor," I answered.
"Oh," he said,
and he went back to bed.

Then I had a good idea.
I tied one end of my cowboy rope
to the bear's tooth
and tied the other end to the bedpost.

194

Then the bear stood on the windowsill
and jumped.

And just as he hit the ground,
the tooth popped out!

The bear was so happy that
he gave me the tooth
to put under my pillow.

Reader's Response

Would you tell your best friend
to read this story?

Writing a Story

You have just read stories that have been told to people all over the world for many years. Think of a story that you have heard or read. How can you share that story with someone else? One way to share it is to write it down on paper.

Getting Ready

All stories have a beginning, a middle, and an end. Look at the box below, and think about the questions to help you plan your story.

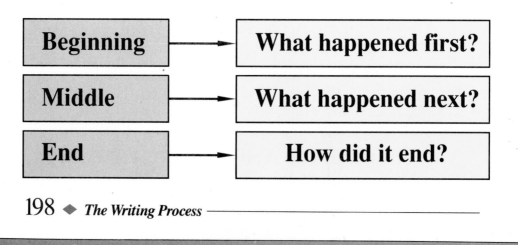

Beginning	→	What happened first?
Middle	→	What happened next?
End	→	How did it end?

Writing

Use the notes in your box to write the story you would like to share. Write what happened first. Write what happened next. End your story with what happened last.

Listening to My Writing

Read your story to a partner. Does your partner know what happened? Tell things more clearly if you need to.

Sharing

Everyone's stories can go into a class book. Call your book *Stories We Know*.

Making up a New Ending

The stories in this unit have been told over and over. When people retell a story, they sometimes change it. You and someone else in your class will now make up a new ending for a story in this unit.

Remember to:

♦ Take turns giving ideas.
♦ Listen when the other person talks.

First, think of the stories in this unit. Decide together what story you will pick. With your partner think of some new endings for the story. Talk about them. Decide on one new ending for the story. Take turns telling the story with its new ending.

Why the Sun and the Moon Live in the Sky by Elphinstone Dayrell *(Houghton Mifflin, 1969)*. This African folktale tells how the moon and sun came to live in the sky.

Morris Tells Boris Mother Moose Stories and Rhymes by Bernard Wiseman *(Dodd, Mead, 1979)*. Boris the Bear can't sleep, so Morris the Moose tells him funny Mother Moose rhymes and stories.

Red Riding Hood retold by James Marshall *(Dial Books, 1987)*. A little girl visits her sick grandmother and meets a stranger.

BROWSING FOR BOOKS

A Place to Read

Do you ever " curl up with a good book "? It is something almost everyone does from time to time. When you are tired, a book can be your very best friend.

Many people have special places where they go to read their books, or just to look at the pictures in them. Do you? Beds are *wonderful* places to read when it's cold and you want to stay cozy and warm. The soft grass under a shady tree can be a fine place to stay cool with a good book. You can also keep a book in the car for the times when there's nothing to look at out the window. Sometimes it's nice to snuggle up to someone older who can read a book *to* you.

The most important thing is not where you read, but that you read something every day. Books can be your friends for life.

Dreams

EZRA JACK KEATS

203

It was hot.
After supper Roberto came
to his window to talk with Amy.
"Look what I made in school today—
a paper mouse!"

"Does it do anything?" Amy asked.

Roberto thought for a while.
"I don't know," he said. Then he put
the mouse on the window sill.

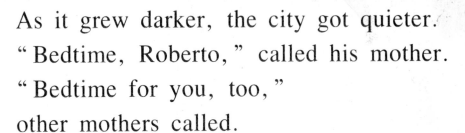

As it grew darker, the city got quieter.
"Bedtime, Roberto," called his mother.
"Bedtime for you, too,"
other mothers called.
"Good-night, Amy."
"Good-night, Roberto."
"G-o-o-o-o-d-night!" echoed the parrot.
Soon they were all in bed.

Someone began to dream.

Soon everybody was dreaming—except one person.

211

Somehow Roberto just couldn't
fall asleep.
It got later and later.

Finally he got up
and went to the window.
What he saw down in the street
made him gasp!

There was Archie's cat!
A big dog had chased him into a box.
The dog snarled.
"He's trapped!" thought Roberto.
"What should I do?"

Then it happened!
His pajama sleeve
brushed the paper mouse
off the window sill.
It sailed away from him.

Down it fell,
turning this way
and that,
casting a big shadow
on the wall.

The shadow grew bigger–
and bigger–

223

and BIGGER!
The dog howled and ran away.

The cat dashed across the street
and jumped through Archie's open window.
"Wow! Wait till I tell Archie
what happened!"
thought Roberto.
"That was some mouse!"
He yawned and went back to bed.

Morning came and everybody
was getting up.
Except one person.

Roberto was fast asleep,
dreaming.

adventures ◇ **artist**

A

adventures There are many adventures in books.

afternoon My party is this afternoon.

against Mother said, "Don't hit the ball against the house."

ago Grandma was born a long time ago.

alone Mark sat alone in the new class.

also Cats like fish. They also like milk.

Americans The people who live in the United States are Americans.

another Sue moved to another state.

anyone That dog will come to anyone.

anywhere Sara does not go anywhere without asking her mother.

artist The artist has paintings.

Americans

artist

B

baked Mother baked bread in the oven.

barn In winter, cows live inside a barn.

basket My dog likes to sleep in his basket.

beanstalk The beanstalk grew very tall.

because It's wet because it just rained.

been Have you been to the lake?

before I brush my teeth before bed.

began Jake began to paint the wall.

better I liked this book better than that one.

birthday Lana baked a birthday cake for her mother.

blind Jeff cannot see because he was born blind.

boat Sam likes to fish from a boat on the river.

baked

barn

my dog's **basket**

Jake **began** to paint.

cart

boy Pete is the new boy in our class.

bread We make toast from bread.

C

---

cart It's easy to move things in a cart.

chair The cat is sitting on the chair.

child Daniel is still a child. He is six years old.

colored The fish were brightly colored.

coming Some friends are coming to play.

cooked Dad got the food ready and cooked dinner.

count Can you count the numbers from one to twenty?

country Rachel lives on a farm in the country.

cousin Dan is my uncle. His son, Rob, is my cousin.

We are **coming**.

Dad **cooked** dinner.

country

D

dancing Pat likes dancing to fast music.

dear The letter said, "Dear Pete, We miss you."

dinner Dinner is the biggest meal of the day.

drank Steve drank a glass of milk.

drums Rick likes to beat on the drums.

ducklings The ducklings all stayed near the mother duck.

dancing

drums

E

empty I need an empty box to pack my books.

enough That was a big dinner. I had enough to eat.

erase If you make a mistake, erase it.

ducklings

erase

235

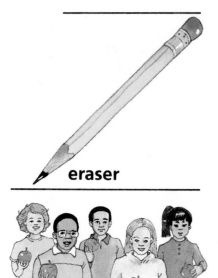

eraser

extra

eraser This pencil has an eraser to rub out mistakes.

even We will have our picnic even if it rains.

everything Everything Deb wears is pink.

everywhere John lost his ball. He looked everywhere for it.

extra Jane wanted the extra apple.

F

family

Ann **felt** the fur.

family My father, my mother, and I are the only three people in my family.

famous Our shop is famous because so many people know about it.

far It takes a long time to walk to the park because it is far away.

favorites The pink and blue bows are my favorites.

felt Ann felt the cat's soft fur.

fingers Grandma's fingers are very thin.

fisherman That fisherman has lots of fish.

forget Don't forget to feed the fish.

forgot Sara forgot to tie her shoes.

four There are two boys and two girls on the grass. Altogether there are four children.

four children

G

---

garden Corn, lettuce, and tomatoes grow in my garden.

girl The little girl was drawing.

goes Helen was running for the bus, but missed it. "There goes the bus," she said.

golden The setting sun gave everything a golden color.

good-by As she left, Nancy kissed her grandpa good-by.

garden

girl

There **goes** the bus.

237

painted

pictures

pitcher

prince

P

painted Lee painted a little house.

paper Fran wrote a letter on white paper.

pencil I like to draw with a pencil.

people Many people can ride on a bus.

pictures Jim has pictures hanging on his walls.

pitcher The pitcher was full.

poor This poor cat has hurt its paw.

prince The prince goes to school, too.

R

remember Can you remember when you were two years old?

road The car drove along the road.

242

S

sausage I ate a sausage with my pancakes.

says The dentist says that my teeth are fine.

second Beth was first in the race, and Mark was second.

share I share my pillow with my doll.

should You should eat three meals a day.

sighs Mother sighs when she is tired.

sight Eric watched the plane until it flew out of sight.

silly Gary was wearing a silly purple and green hat.

simple Megan likes to make simple clothes.

slipped The bear slipped on the ice and almost fell down.

smiles Lee smiles when he is happy.

I **share** my pillow.

making **simple** clothes

slipped

243

stopped

storyteller

summer

surprises

soft The pillow feels very soft.

sometimes Rosanne sometimes wears her hair in a bow.

sorry Pete was sorry that he had broken the dish.

soup I like to drink soup from a cup.

special Tim wore his special shirt to the party.

splash The dog jumped into the lake with a splash.

stamps This letter needs more stamps.

stood When he saw the snake, Brad stood very still.

stopped The car stopped at the light.

storyteller The storyteller told them many great stories.

straight This stick is crooked, but that one is straight.

summer It is warm in summer. We wear shorts every day.

surprises I had two surprises today. Two frogs jumped out of my bag.

T

table We set the table for dinner.

tadpoles We catch tadpoles to watch them turn into frogs.

talked Everyone talked and shouted at the same time.

teach The teacher will teach us many things.

tears John had tears in his eyes as he said good-by.

tents When my family went camping, we stayed in three tents.

third Tad won the race. Matt was second, and Jed came in third.

through The dog walked through the door.

tiny An ant is a tiny animal.

together Let's have our picnic together.

town A town has many houses in it.

toy The dog likes to play with his toy.

travelers Many travelers enjoy camping.

tadpoles

teach

tents

the dog's **toy**

The top **turned**.

turnip

tries Susan tries to make cakes. They usually taste great!

turned Jerry watched as the top turned.

turnip You can buy a turnip in a vegetable shop.

twice Fred was at bat two times. He hit the ball twice.

U

used Meg used a broom to sweep up the leaves.

village

V

village Helen lives in a village with only nine houses.

visit Lee goes to visit her grandparents every week.

Lee goes to **visit**.

W

wear Beth likes to wear her red dress.

whistles The man uses whistles to call his dogs.

white New snow is white.

whoever Whoever wins the race will win the prize.

wife Mr. Rodrigo lives with his wife, Mrs. Rodrigo.

wisely John is careful with his money and spends it wisely.

woman The little girl wants to grow up and become a woman.

woods Many trees grow in the woods.

words There are many words in this book.

write Joe likes to write letters to his friends.

wrote Joe wrote four letters yesterday.

girl and **woman**

woods

This book has **words.**

Y

yourself Do you ever talk to yourself?

write

WORD LIST

The following story critical words appear in *A New Day*. The words are listed next to the number of the page on which they first appear.

Unit 1

Your Friend, Little Bear

11 summer
good-by
baked
lemonade

12 drank
talked

17 learn
write

Alone

24 alone

26 island

27 everything

31 sorry

33 felt
because

A New Day in the City

44 I'm

46 surprises
paper
painted
family

47 pictures

48 together

Together

53 blind
words

55 fingers
special

56 own

58 share

Goldfish and Lee

67 visit
teach
horse

68 before
says

69 smiles

70 tries

71 soft

We Are Best Friends

79 news

81 moved

83 letter

84 lonely

85 boy

88 tadpoles

These authors have written some of the stories in this book.

VERNA AARDEMA

VERNA AARDEMA

Verna Aardema's first stories were the ones she made up for her daughter. Now her stories are read by children all over the world. *(Born 1911)*

ALIKI

ALIKI

Aliki's full name is Aliki Liacouras Brandenberg. Aliki says, "I write two kinds of books–fiction (which comes from my own ideas) and nonfiction (which I must find out about from others)." She also draws pictures for books.

NIKKI GIOVANNI

Nikki Giovanni writes poetry. She says she likes to write for children and to read to children. She says she wants her poetry to touch their hearts and minds. Nikki Giovanni also hopes that adults will like her poetry. *(Born 1943)*

NIKKI GIOVANNI

EZRA JACK KEATS

Ezra Jack Keats wrote many books. He also illustrated books. He began painting when he was about four years old. Ezra Jack Keats won many awards for his work. *(1916–1983)*

EZRA JACK KEATS

ANNE ROCKWELL

ANNE ROCKWELL

Anne Rockwell writes books for children. She also illustrates books. She says she has a special place to write her books. It is a "secret writing room for me, with a window that looks up only into the trees. I have been having a wonderful time working in it." *(Born 1934)*

ALVIN SCHWARTZ

ALVIN SCHWARTZ

Alvin Schwartz writes books for children. He likes to write in a small space. He says, "I write in a small outbuilding which is 8 feet by 8 feet but almost all windows." Several of his books have been selected as American Library Association Notable Books. *(Born 1927)*

AUTHOR INDEX